Mel Bay's

CLASSIC MELODIES ENCYCLOPEDIA

CONTENTS

C

D

E

F

G

H

I

S

T

V

W

IL BACIO

L. Arditi

くちづけ

TANGO IN D

I. Albéniz

SUITE No.2—RONDO

ロンド

J. S. Bach

SUITE No.2—POLONAISE

ポロネーズ

J. S. Bach

SUITE No.2—BADINERIE

バディネリー

J. S. Bach

ENGLISH SUITE-PRELUDE
プレリュード

J. S. Bach

AIR ON THE G-STRING
G線上のアリア

J. S. Bach

13

MENUET

J. S. Bach

MENUET

J. S. Bach

MUSETTE

J. S. Bach

ミュゼット

MARCHE (Anna Magdalena Bach)

マ ー チ

J. S. Bach

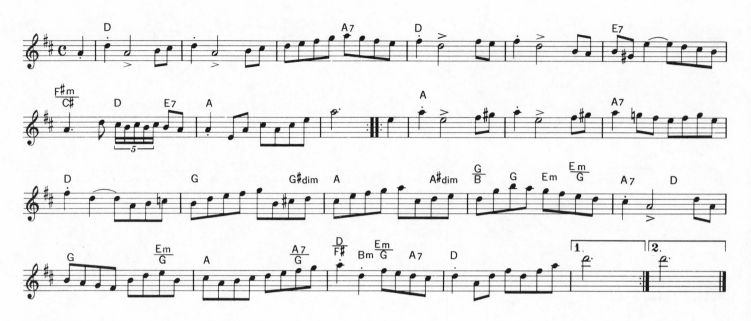

BOURRÉE (Anna Magdalena Bach)

ブ ー レ ー

J. S. Bach

INVENTIONS No.1

J. S. Bach

インヴェンション

INVENTIONS No.2

J. S. Bach

インヴェンション

INVENTIONS No.4

J. S. Bach

INVENTIONS No.8

J. S. Bach

TOCCATA UND FUGE IN D MOLL

J. S. Bach

トッカータとフーガ ニ短調

BRANDENBURG CONCERTOS No.5 (1st Movement)

J. S. Bach

ブランデンブルグ協奏曲

BRANDENBURG CONCERTOS No.5 (3rd Movement)

J. S. Bach

ITALIENISCHES KONZERT

J. S. Bach

イタリア風協奏曲

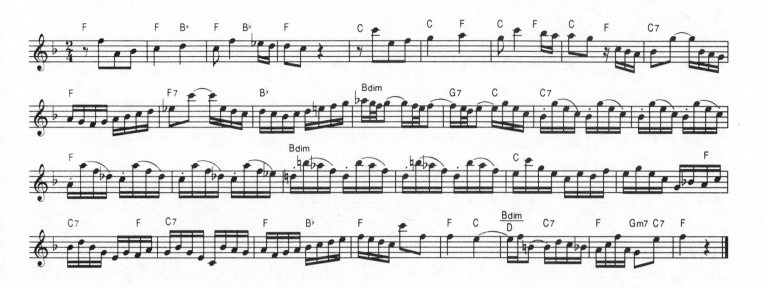

GOLDBERG-VARIATIONEN

J. S. Bach

ゴルトベルク変奏曲--主題

20

WOHLMIR, DAß ICH JESUM HABE, BWV.147

J. S. Bach

主よ人の望みの喜びよ

KLEINE FUGE IN G MOLL

J. S. Bach

小フーガ ト短調

GAVOTTE IN B MOLL

ガボット　ロ短調

J. S. Bach

GAVOTTE IN D

ガボット　ニ長調

J. S. Bach

BOURRÉE

ブーレー

J. S. Bach

GEBET EINER JUNGFRAU

乙女の祈り

T. Badarzewska

SYMPHONY No.3-EROICA (1st Movement)

L. v. Beethoven

英　雄

SYMPHONY No.3-EROICA (2nd Movement)

L. v. Beethoven

SYMPHONY No.3-EROICA (4th Movement)

L. v. Beethoven

SYMPHONY No.5 (1st Movement)

L. v. Beethoven

運　命

SYMPHONY No.5 (2nd Movement)

L. v. Beethoven

SYMPHONY No.5 (3rd Movement)

L. v. Beethoven

SYMPHONY No.5 (4th Movement)

L. v. Beethoven

SYMPHONY No.6-PASTORALE (1st Movement)

L. v. Beethoven

田 園

SYMPHONY No.6-PASTORALE (3rd Movement)

L. v. Beethoven

SYMPHONY No.6-PASTORALE (5th Movement)

L. v. Beethoven

SYMPHONY No.7 (2nd Movement)

L. v. Beethoven

SYMPHONY No.8 (1st Movement)

L. v. Beethoven

SYMPHONY No.9-CHORAL (1st Movement)

L. v. Beethoven

合　唱

SYMPHONY No.9-CHORAL (2nd Movement)

L. v. Beethoven

SYMPHONY No.9-CHORAL (3rd Movement)

L. v. Beethoven

SYMPHONY No.9-CHORAL (4th Movement)

L. v. Beethoven

EGMONT OVERTURE

エグモント序曲

L. v. Beethoven

CORIOLAN OVERTURE

コリオラン序曲

L. v. Beethoven

PIANO CONCERTO No.3 (1st Movement)

L. v. Beethoven

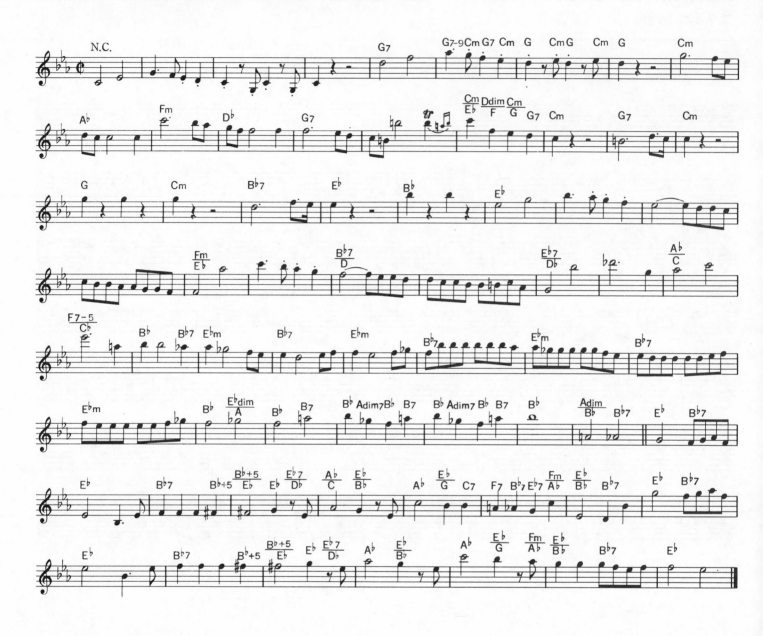

PIANO CONCERTO No.3 (3rd Movement)

L. v. Beethoven

PIANO CONCERTO No.5—EMPEROR (1st Movement)

L. v. Beethoven

皇　帝

PIANO CONCERTO No.5—EMPEROR (2nd Movement)

L. v. Beethoven

PIANO SONATA—PATHÉTIQUE (1st Movement)

L. v. Beethoven

PIANO SONATA—PATHÉTIQUE (2nd Movement)

L. v. Beethoven

PIANO SONATA—PATHÉTIQUE (3rd Movement)

L. v. Beethoven

PIANO SONATA-WALDSTEIN (1st Movement)

L. v. Beethoven

ワルトシュタイン

PIANO SONATA—APPASSIONATA (1st Movement)

L. v. Beethoven

熱 情

PIANO SONATA—APPASSIONATA (2nd Movement)

L. v. Beethoven

VIOLIN SONATA—SPRING (1st Movement)

春

L. v. Beethoven

VIOLIN SONATA—SPRING (3rd Movement)

L. v. Beethoven

VIOLIN SONATA—SPRING (4th Movement)

L. v. Beethoven

STRINGS QUARTET Op.59 No.3 "RASOUMOWSKY"

L. v. Beethoven

ラズモフスキー第3番

VIOLIN CONCERTO Op.61 (1st Movement)

L. v. Beethoven

Allegro ma non troppo

ROMANZE IN F

L. v. Beethoven

へ調のロマンス

ROMANCE IN G

L. v. Beethoven

ト調のロマンス

MOON LIGHT SONATA

L. v. Beethoven

月　光

SONATINE IN G (1st Movement)

L. v. Beethoven

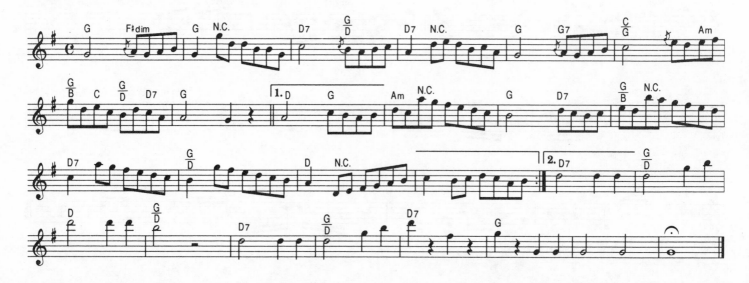

FÜR ELISE

L. v. Beethoven

エリーゼのために

ECOSSAISE

L. v. Beethoven

エコセーズ

TURKISH MARCH

L. v. Beethoven

トルコ行進曲

MINUET IN G

L. v. Beethoven

メヌエット ト長調

ICH LIEBE DICH

L. v. Beethoven

あなたを愛す

RAKOCZY MARCH (HUNGARIAN MARCH)

H. Berlioz

ラコッツィ・マーチ

L'ARLÉSIENNE SUITE No.1—MENUET

G. Bizet

アルルの女―メヌエット

L'ARLÉSIENNE SUITE No.1—PRELUDE

G. Bizet

プレリュード 前奏曲

L'ARLÉSIENNE SUITE No.2—INTERMEZZO

G. Bizet

インテルメッツォ 間奏曲

L'ARLÉSIENNE SUITE No.2—PASTORALE

G. Bizet

パストラーレ 牧歌

CARMEN—HABANERA

G. Bizet

ハバネラ

CARMEN—TORÉADOR

G. Bizet

闘牛士の歌

CARMEN—DANSE BOHÈME

ジプシーの踊り

G. Bizet

CARMEN—PRELUDE

前奏曲

G. Bizet

CARMEN—CASTANET SONG

G. Bizet

カスタネットの歌

SPANISH SERENADE

G. Bizet

スペインのセレナード

MENUETTO

L. Boccherini

ANGEL'S SERENADE

G.Braga

天使のセレナード

WALTZ OF THE VIOLETS

K. Bohm

スミレのワルツ

LA ZINGANA

K. Bohm

ジプシーの歌

EINE STEPPENSKIZZE AUS MITTEL-ASIEN

A. Borodin

中央アジアの草原にて

POLOVETZIAN DANCE (1st Theme)

A. Borodin

ダッタン人の踊り

POLOVETZIAN DANCE (3rd Theme)

A. Borodin

NOCTURNE

A. Borodin

ノクターン

58

SYMPHONY No.1 (1st Movement)

J. Brahms

SYMPHONY No.1 (2nd Movement)

J. Brahms

SYMPHONY No.1 (4th Movement)

J. Brahms

AKADEMISCHE FESTOUVERTÜRE

J. Brahms

大学祝典序曲

SYMPHONY No.3 (3rd Movement)

J. Brahms

SYMPHONY No.4 (1st Movement)

J. Brahms

SYMPHONY No.4 (2nd Movement)

J. Brahms

HUNGARIAN DANCES No.1

J. Brahms

ハンガリア舞曲

HUNGARIAN DANCES No.2

J. Brahms

HUNGARIAN DANCES No.4

J. Brahms

HUNGARIAN DANCES No.5

J. Brahms

HUNGARIAN DANCES No.6

J. Brahms

VIOLIN CONCERTO IN D (2nd Movement)

J. Brahms

CLARINET QUINTET Op.115 (1st Movement)

J. Brahms

WALTZ

J. Brahms

CELEBRATED WALTZES

J. Brahms

祝典ワルツ

WIEGENLIED
子 守 歌

J. Brahms

SANDMÄNNCHEN
眠りの精

J. Brahms

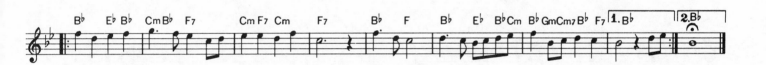

VON EWIGER LIEBE
永遠の愛

J. Brahms

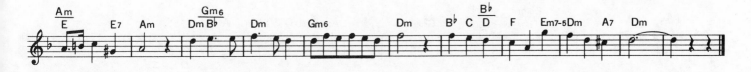

MINNELIED

J. Brahms

愛 の 歌

MARIA! MARI!

E. d. Capua

マリア・マリ

PIANO CONCERTO (1st Movement)

F. Chopin

ETUDE Op.10 No.3

F. Chopin

別 れ の 曲

68

ETUDE Op.25 No.9

F. Chopin

PRELUDE Op.28 No.4

F. Chopin

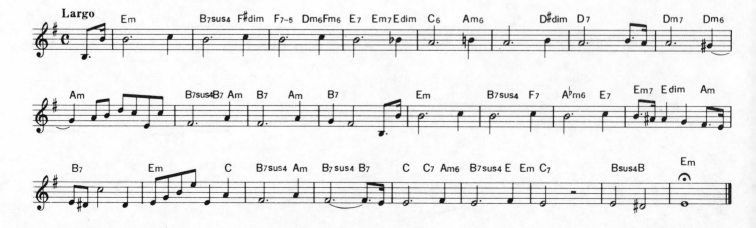

PRÉLUDE Op.28 No.7

F. Chopin

PRELUDE Op.28 No.15

F. Chopin

雨 だ れ

PRELUDE Op.28 No.20

F. Chopin

POLONAISE Op.40 No.1

軍　　隊

F. Chopin

POLONAISE Op.53

英　　雄

F. Chopin

BALLADE Op.23

F. Chopin

PIANO SONATA Op.35 (TRAUERMARSCH)

F. Chopin

葬送行進曲

VALSE Op.34 No.1

F. Chopin

VALSE Op.34 No.2

F. Chopin

VALSE Op.POSTH

F. Chopin

ワルツー遺作

VALSE Op.64 No.1

小犬のワルツ

F. Chopin

VALSE Op.64 No.2

F. Chopin

VALSE Op.69 No.1

F. Chopin

VALSE Op.69 No.2

F. Chopin

MAZURKA Op.7 No.1

F. Chopin

MAZURKA Op.7 No.2

F. Chopin

MAZURKA Op.33 No.4

F. Chopin

MAZURKA Op.33 No.2

F. Chopin

MAZURKA Op.33 No.3

F. Chopin

MAZURKA Op.24 No.3

F. Chopin

NOCTURNE Op.9 No.2

F. Chopin

NOCTURNE Op.15 No.2

F. Chopin

NOCTURNE Op.27 No.2

F. Chopin

NOCTURNE Op.15 No.3

F. Chopin

NOCTURNE Op.32 No.1

F. Chopin

BERCEUSE Op.57

F. Chopin

子 守 歌

GRANDE VALSE BRILLANTE

F. Chopin

華麗なる大円舞曲

FANTAISIE-IMPROMPTU

幻想即興曲

F. Chopin

MÄDCHENS WUNSH

乙女の願い

F. Chopin

84

RONDO

F. Couperin

ORIENTALE

C. Cui

オリエンタル

LOVE'S DREAM AFTER THE BALL

A. Czibulka

舞踏会のあとの愛の夢

STEPHANI GAVOTTE

A. Czibulka

ステファニー・ガボット

LA FILLE AUX CHEVEUX DE LIN

亜麻色の髪の乙女

C. Debussy

CLAIR DE LUNE

月 の 光

C. Debussy

ARABESQUE No.1

C. Debussy

アラベスク

REVERIE

C. Debussy

夢

EN BATEAU
小舟にて

C. Debussy

GOLLIWOG'S CAKEWALK
子供の領分　ゴリウォッグのケークウォーク

C. Debussy

SYLVIA—PIZZICATO

シルヴィアのピチカート

L. Delibes

COPPELIA—WALTZ

コッペリアのワルツ

L. Delibes

MAZURUKA

L. Delibes

D.C. al Fine

MAIDS OF CADIZ

L. Delibes

カディスの娘たち

LI'SIR D'AMORE—UNA FURTIVA LAGRIM

G. Donizetti

人知れぬ涙

SERENADE

ドリゴのセレナーデ

R. Drigo

POMPONETTE

A. Durand

WALSE IN E♭

A. Durand

SYMPHONY No.7 (3rd Movement)

A. Dvořák

SYMPHONY No.9-NEW WORLD (2nd Movement)

新世界より

A. Dvořák

STRINGS QUARTET No.6 "AMERICAN" (1st Movement)

アメリカ

A. Dvořák

SYMPHONY No.8 (3rd Movement)

A. Dvořák

イ ギ リ ス

SONGS MY MOTHER TAUGHT ME

A. Dvořák

わが母の教えたまいし歌

VALSE GRACIEUSE

A. Dvořák

優雅なワルツ

HUMORESKE

A. Dvořák

ユーモレスク

SLAVONIC DANCES

A. Dvořák

スラブ舞曲

DIE MÜHLE IN SCHWARZWALD

R. Eilenberg

森 の 水 車

APRÉS UN RÊVE
夢のあとに

G. U. Fauré

SICILIENNE
シチリアーノ

G. U. Fauré

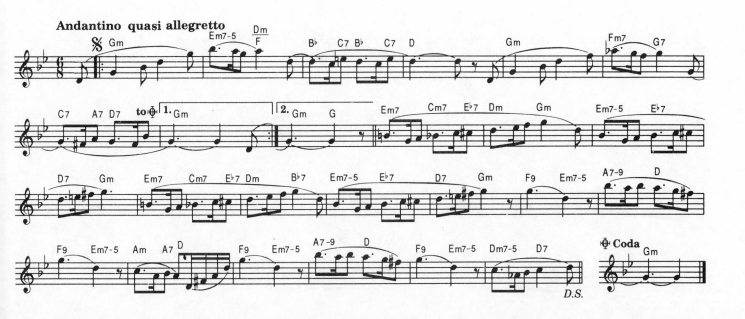

100

BERCEUSE

ドリー―子守歌

G. U. Fauré

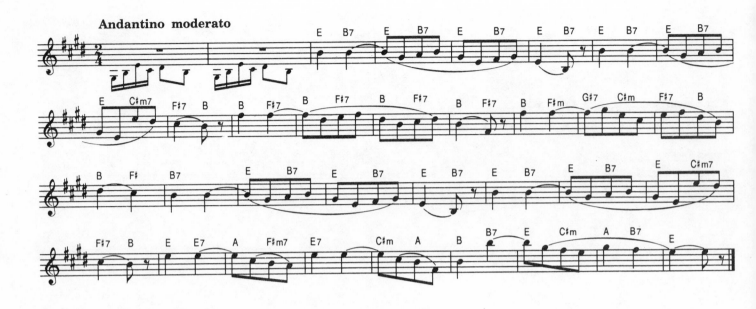

MARTHA—M'APPARI TUTT'AMOR

マルタ―夢のごとく

F. v. Flotow

OVERTURE FROM MARTHA

F. v. Flotow

マルタ―序曲

VIOLIN SONATA (1st Movement)

C. Franck

AMARYLLIS

J. Ghys

アマリリス

CARO MIO BEN

G. Giordani

カロ・ミオ・ベン

DANCE OF SPAIRITS

C. W. Gluck

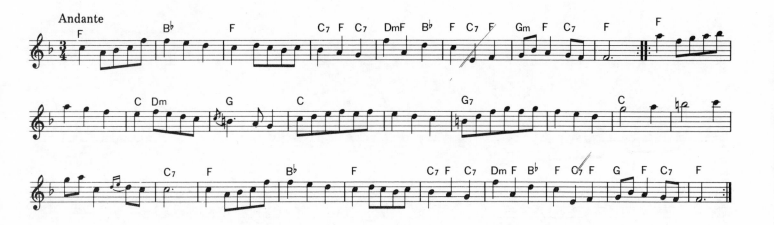

GAVOTTE

C. W. Gluck

BERCEUSE

ジョスランの子守歌

B. Godard

GAVOTTE

F. J. Gossec

FAUST—WALTZ

ファウスト―ワルツ

C. Gounod

FAUST—CHOEUR DES FILLES

C. Gounod

暁 の 歌

BALLET MUSIC No.1

舞　曲

C. Gounod

Moderato Waltz

BALLET MUSIC No.6

C. Gounod

AVE MARIA

アヴェ・マリア

C. Gounod

SERENADE
夜 の 調 べ

C. Gounod

ANITRA'S DANCE
アニトラの踊り

E. Grieg

SOLVEJG'S LIED

E. Grieg

ソルヴェーグの歌

ASES TOD

E. Grieg

オーゼの死

MORGENSTIMMUNG

朝

E. Grieg

IN DER HALLE DES BERGKÖNIGS

山上の宮殿にて

E. Grieg

NORWEGIAN DANCES

E. Grieg

ノルウェー・ダンス

PIANO CONCERTO A MOLL (1st Movement)

E. Grieg

ANDALUZA

アンダルーサ

E. Granados

WALTZ Op.101 No.1

C. Gurlitt

LARGO

ラルゴ

G. F. Händel

HALLELUJAH

ハレルヤ

G. F. Händel

BOURRÉE

G. F. Händel

ブーレー

HARMONIOUS BLACKSMITH

G. F. Händel

調子のよいかじ屋

116

WATER MUSIC

水上の音楽

G. F. Händel

HORNPIPE

ホーンパイプ

G. F. Händel

JUDAS MACCABAÜS

勇者は帰りぬ

G. F. Händel

SERENADE

F. J. Haydn

QUARTET No.5—LERCHEN

ひ　ば　り

F. J. Haydn

QUARTET No.3—KAISER (2nd Movement)

皇　帝

F. J. Haydn

SYNFONIA No.45 "ABSCHIED"

告　別

F. J. Haydn

SYMPHONY No.94—SUPRISE (2nd Movement)

F. J. Haydn

驚　愕

SYMPHONY No.100—MILITÄR (1st Movement)

F. J. Haydn

軍　隊

SYMPHONY No.101-CLOCK (2nd Movement)

時　　計

F. J. Haydn

PIANO SONATA IN C (1st Movement)

F. J. Haydn

GIPSY ROND

ジプシー・ロンド

F. J. Haydn

OUVERTÜRE "HÄNSEL UND GRETEL"

E. Humperdinck

ヘンゼルとグレーテル―序曲

PROCESSION OF THE SARDAR

M. Ippolitov-Ivanov

酋長の行列

WAVES OF THE DANUBE

ドナウ川のさざなみ

J. Ivanovici

ROCKED IN THE CRADLE OF THE DEEP

たゆとう小舟

J. P. Knight

SYMPHONIE ESPAGNOLE (1st Movement)

スペイン交響曲

E. Lalo

126

FLOWER SONG

花 の 歌

G. Lange

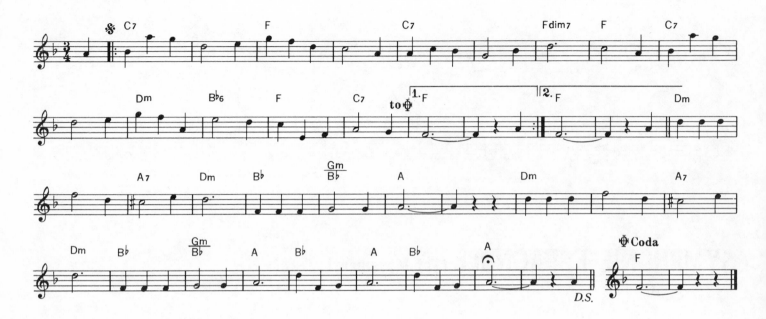

HEATHER ROSE

G. Lange

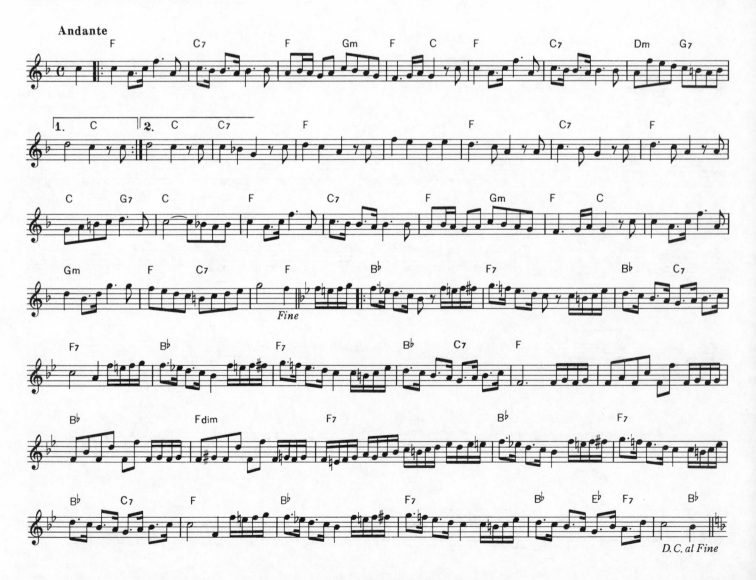

MATTINATA

朝 の 歌

R.Leoncavallo

PAGLIACCI VESTI LA GIUBBA

R.Leoncavallo

衣装をつけろ

128

LA CAMPANELLA

鐘

F. Liszt

LIEBESTRAUM No.3

愛の夢

F. Liszt

HUNGARIAN RHAPSODY No.2

F. Liszt

ハンガリアン・ラプソディー

CONSOLATION No.2

F. Liszt

コンソレーション

HUNGARIAN RHAPSODY No.6

F. Liszt

WOODLAND SKETCHES No.1

森のスケッチ―野ばらに

E. MacDowell

Moderato

WOODLAND SKETCHES No.3

昔ふたりが会った所で

E. MacDowell

Moderato

WOODLAND SKETCHES No.4

E. MacDowell

秋　に

PIACER D'AMOR

T. Martini

愛 の 喜び

LOVE IN IDLENESS

三色すみれ

A. Macbeth

THAIS—MEDITATION

タイスの冥想曲

J. Massenet

SYMPHONY No.1 "DER TITAN" (1st Movement)

巨　　人

G. Mahler

ELEGIE

エ　レ　ジ　ー

J. Massenet

AMERICAN PATROL

アメリカン・パトロール

F. W. Meacham

Tempo di Marcia

SYMPHONY No.4-ITALIA (1st Movement)

イタリア

F. Mendelssohn

THA FINGAL'S CAVE

F. Mendelssohn

フィンガルの洞窟

WEDDING MARCH

F. Mendelssohn

結婚行進曲

NOCTURNE
ノクターン

F. Mendelssohn

VIOLIN CONCERTO (1st Movement)

F. Mendelssohn

VIOLIN CONCERTO (2nd Movement)

F. Mendelssohn

SCHERZO IN E MOLL

F. Mendelssohn

スケルツォ

AUF FLÜGELN DES GESANGES

F. Mendelssohn

歌 の 翼 に

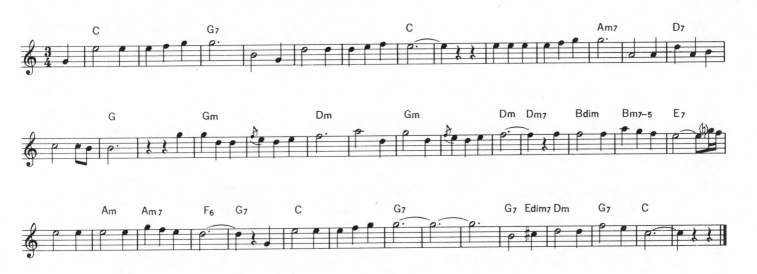

LIEDER OHNE WORTE Op.30 No.6

F. Mendelssohn

ベニスの舟歌

LIEDER OHNE WORTE Op.62 No.6

春 の 歌

F. Mendelssohn

LIEDER OHNE WORTE Op.67 No.4

F. Mendelssohn

紡ぎ歌

LOVE'S OLD SWEET SONG

J. L. Molloy

なつかしき愛の歌

LA CINQUANTAINE

金 婚 式

G. Merie

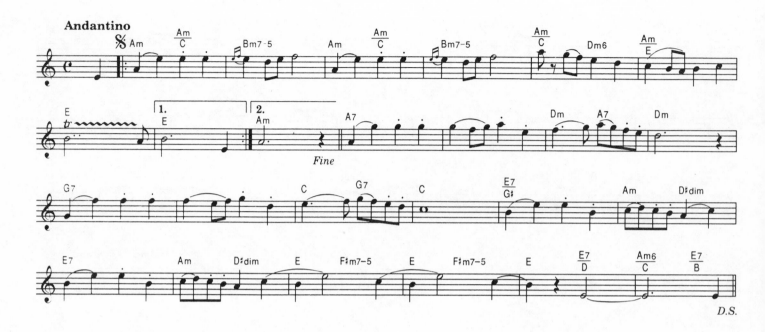

CSÁRDÁS

チャルダッシュ

V. Monti

BLACKSMITH IN THE WOODS

森のかじや

T. Michaelis

TOY SYMPHONY (1st Movement)

L. Mozart

おもちゃの交響曲

TOY SYMPHONY (2nd Movement)

L. Mozart

TOY SYMPHONY (3rd Movement)

L. Mozart

SYMPHONY No.36-LINZ (1st Movement)

W. A. Mozart

リ ン ツ

SYMPHONY No.38—PRAG (1st Movement)

プ ラ ハ

W. A. Mozart

SYMPHONY No.39 (1st Movement)

W. A. Mozart

SYMPHONY No.39 (4th Movement)

W. A. Mozart

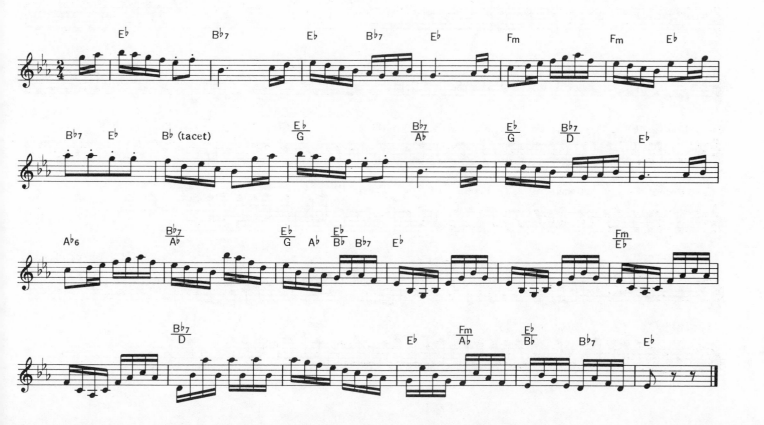

SYMPHONY No.40 (1st Movement)

W. A. Mozart

SYMPHONY No.40 (3rd Movement)

W. A. Mozart

SYMPHONY No.41-JUPITER (1st Movement)

W. A. Mozart

ジュピター

SYMPHONY No.41—JUPITER (2nd Movement)

ジュピター

W. A. Mozart

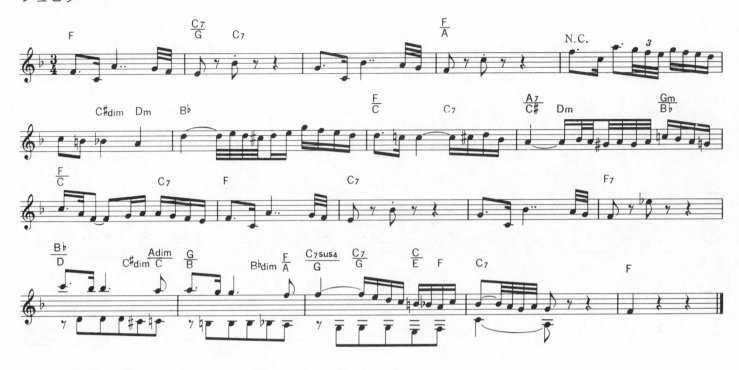

SYMPHONY No.41-JUPITER (3rd Movement)

W. A. Mozart

PIANO CONCERTO K.467 (1st Movement)

W. A. Mozart

PIANO CONCERTO K.467 (2nd Movement)

W. A. Mozart

PIANO CONCERTO K.466 (2nd Movement)

W. A. Mozart

PIANO CONCERTO K.488 (1st Movement)

W. A. Mozart

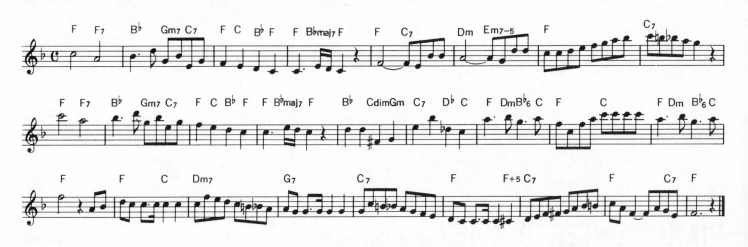

PIANO CONCERTO K.537 (1st Movement)

W. A. Mozart

戴 冠 式

153

PIANO CONCERTO K.537 (2nd Movement)

W. A. Mozart

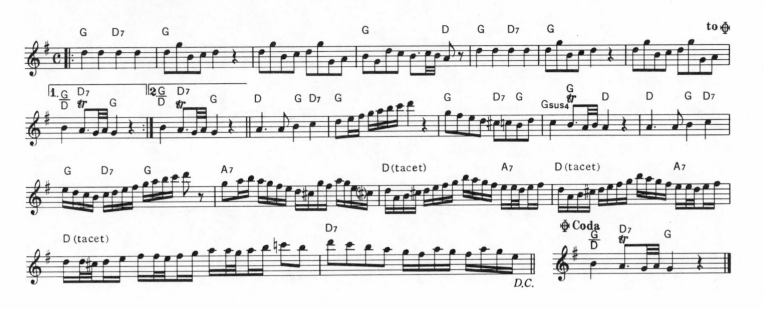

PIANO CONCERTO K.537 (3rd Movement)

W. A. Mozart

VIOLIN CONCERTO No.5 "TURKISH" (3rd Movement)

W. A. Mozart

トルコ風

VIOLIN CONCERTO No.4 (1st Movement)

W. A. Mozart

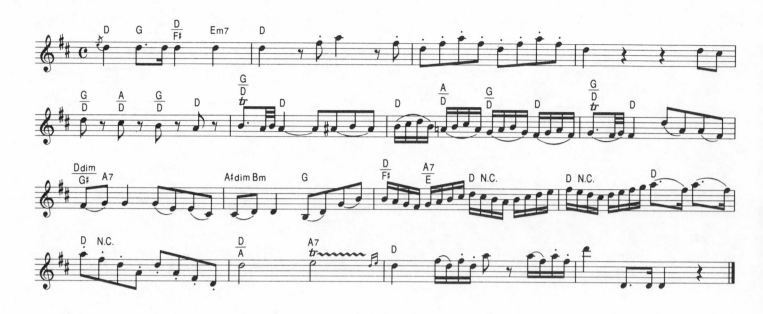

STRINGS QUARTET No.17 "JAGD" (1st Movement)

W. A. Mozart

狩

Allegro vivace assai

CLARINET CONCERTO K.622 (1st Movement)

W. A. Mozart

CLARINET CONCERTO K.622 (2nd Movement)

W. A. Mozart

CLARINET QUINTET K.581 (1st Movement)

クラリネット五重奏曲

W. A. Mozart

FLUTE CONCERTO No.1 (1st Movement)

W. A. Mozart

FLUTE QUARTET K.298 (1st Movement)

W. A. Mozart

CONCERTO FOR FLUTE & HARP K.299 (1st Movement)

W. A. Mozart

HORN CONCERTO No.1 (1st Movement)

W. A. Mozart

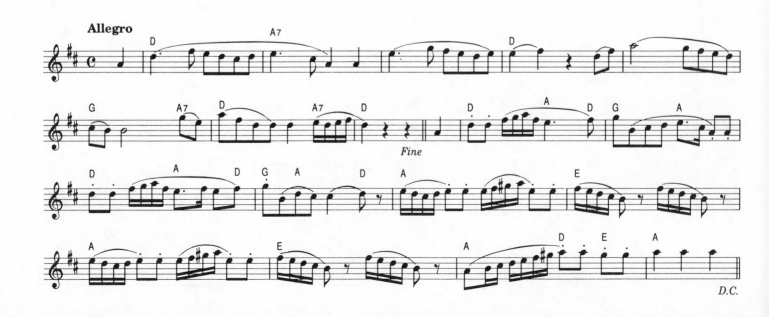

DIE ZAUBERFLÖTE—OVERTURE

W. A. Mozart

魔笛—序曲

DIVERTIMENTO K.136 (1st Movement)

W. A. Mozart

160

DIVERTIMENTO K.334 (3rd Movement)

W. A. Mozart

EINE KLEINE NACHTMUSIK (1st Movement)

W. A. Mozart

アイネ・クライネ・ナハトムジーク

EINE KLEINE NACHTMUSIK (2nd Movement)

W. A. Mozart

EINE KLEINE NACHTMUSIK (3rd Movement)

W. A. Mozart

EINE KLEINE NACHTMUSIK (4th Movement)

W. A. Mozart

PIANO SONATA K.545 (1st Movement)

W. A. Mozart

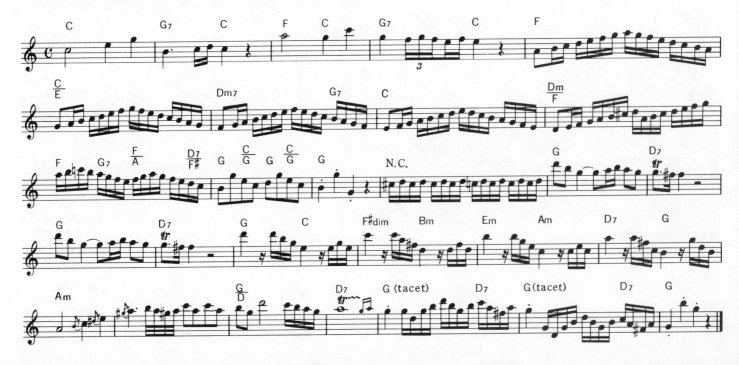

PIANO SONATA K.545 (2nd Movement)

W. A. Mozart

PIANO SONATA K.331 (1st Movement)

W. A. Mozart

PIANO SONATA K.331 (3rd Movement)

W. A. Mozart

トルコ行進曲

PIANO SONATA K.283 (1st Movement)

W. A. Mozart

PIANO SONATA K.309 (1st Movement)

W. A. Mozart

PIANO SONATA K.310 (1st Movement)

W. A. Mozart

VALSE FAVORITE

W. A. Mozart

大好きなワルツ

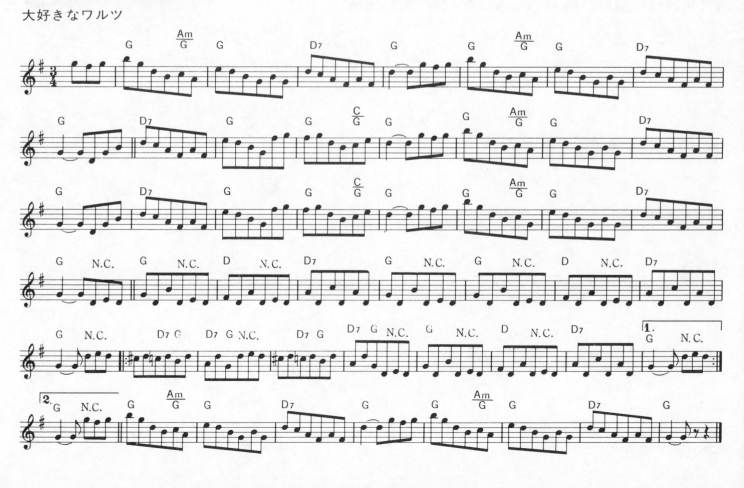

ARIETTA
アリエッタ

W. A. Mozart

LE NOZZE DI FIGARO—OVERTURE
フィガロの結婚—序曲

W. A. Mozart

DON GIOVANNI—MINUET
ドン・ジョバンニ—メヌエット

W. A. Mozart

LE NOZZE DI FIGARO—NON PIÙ ANDRAI

W. A. Mozart

もうとぶまいぞ このちょうちょ

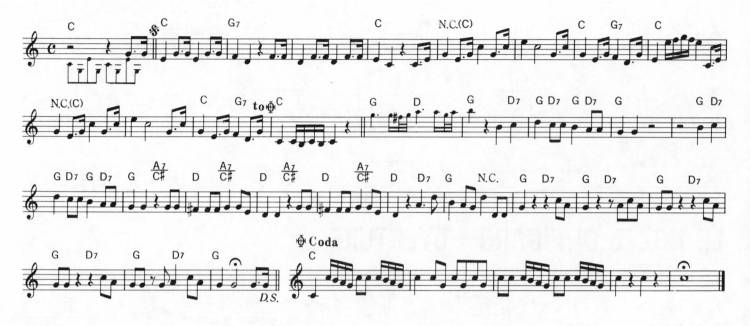

DON GIOVANNI—BATTI, BATTI, O BEL MASETTO

W. A. Mozart

ぶってよマゼット

DON GIOVANNI—LÀ CI DAREM LA MANO

W. A. Mozart

手をとりあって

LE NOZZE DI FIGARO—VIO CHE SAPETE

W. A. Mozart

恋とはどんなものかしら

WIEGENLIED

W. A. Mozart

子 守 歌

DAS VEILCHEN
すみれ

W. A. Mozart

DAUERNDE LIEBE

W. A. Mozart

永遠なる愛

MENUET K.1

W. A. Mozart

MENUET K.2

W. A. Mozart

TABLEAUX D'UNE EXPOSITION (PROMENADE)

M. Mussorgsky

プロムナード

TABLEAUX D'UNE EXPOSITION (LA GRANDE PORTE DE KIEV)

M. Mussorgsky

キエフの大きな門

TABLEAUX D'UNE EXPOSITION (IL VECCHIO CASTELLO)

M. Mussorgsky

古　城

BYDLO

M. Mussorgsky

ブィドロ

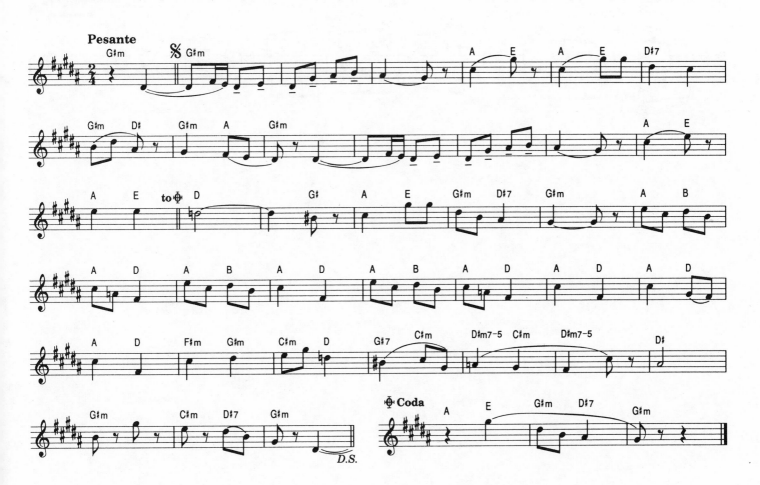

GOPAK

ゴパーク

M. Mussorgsky

174

CSIKOS POST

クシコスの郵便馬車

H. Neck

DOLLY'S DREAMING & AWAKENING

T. Oesten

人形の夢と目覚め

ALPENABENDRÖTE

アルプスの夕映え

T. Oesten

ORPHEUS IN HADES (Can Can)

J. Offenbach

天国と地獄

ORPHEUS IN HADES OVERTURE

天国と地獄—序曲

J. Offenbach

TALES OF HOFFMAN—BARCAROLLE

J. Offenbach

ホフマン物語―ホフマンの舟歌

CAPRICCO PER VIOLINO SOLO Op.1-24

24のカプリスより

N. Paganini

NINA

ニーナの死

G. B. Pergolesi

DANCE OF THE HOURS

時 の 踊 り

A. Ponchielli

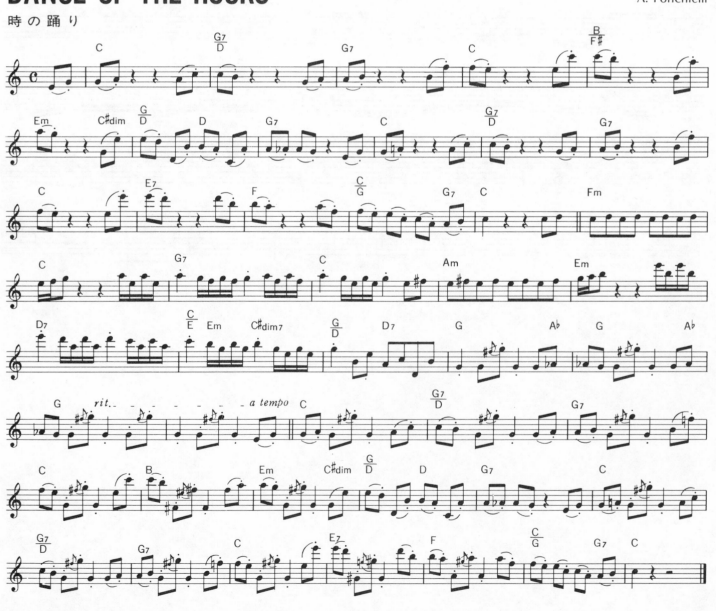

PETER

ピーターと狼—ピーター

S. S. Prokofév

DUCK

ピーターと狼—あひる

S. S. Prokofév

CAT

ピーターと狼—猫

S. S. Prokofév

WOLF

ピーターと狼―狼

S. S. Prokofév

MADAME BUTTERFLY

蝶々夫人―ある晴れた日に

G. Puccini

TOSCA―E LUCEVAN LE STELLE

トスカ―星は輝きぬ

G. Puccini

RIGAUDON
リゴードン

J. Rameau

TAMBOURIN
タンブーラン

J. Rameau

186

SADKO—CHANSON INDOUS

サトコ―インドの歌

N. Rimsky-Korsakov

LE COQ D'OR HYMNE AU SOLEIL

金鶏―太陽の讃歌

N. Rimsky-Korsakov

THE FLIGHT OF BUMBLE-BEE

N. Rimsky-Korsakov

熊蜂の飛行

SCHEHERAZADE

N. Rimsky-Korsakov

シェエラザード

WILLIAM TELL OVERTURE

G. Rossini

ウイリアム・テル序曲―牧歌

BARBIERE DI SIVIGLIA OVERTURE

G. Rossini

セビリアの理髪師―序曲

BARBIERE DI SIVIGLIA—UNA VOCE POCO FA

G. Rossini

今 の 歌声

192

WILLIAM TELL OVERTURE

G. Rossini

ウイリアム・テル序曲―スイス軍の行進

RÊVE ANGÉLIQUE

A. Rubinstein

天使の夢

MELODY IN F

A. Rubinstein

へ調の旋律

ROMANCE

A. Rubinstein

OVER THE WAVES

J. Rosas

波濤を越えて

LE CARNAVAL DE ANIMAUX—LE CYGNE

C. Saint-Saëns

白　　鳥

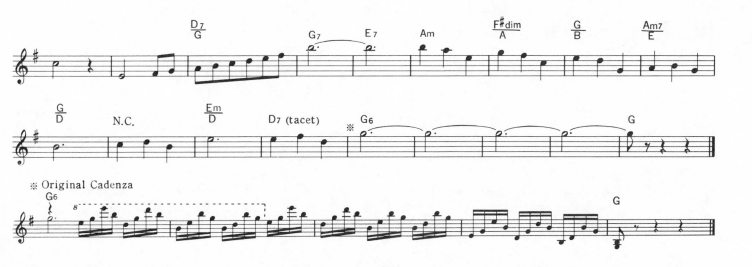

DANSE MACABRE

死 の 舞 踊

C. Saint-Saëns

Valse Moderato

MARCHE ROYALE DU LION

獅子王の行進

C. Saint-Saëns

L'ÉLÉPHANT

象

C. Saint-Saëns

INTRODUCTION ET RONDO CAPRICCIOSO

C. Saint-Saëns

序奏とロンド・カプリチオーソ

ZIGEUNERWEISEN

チゴイネルワイゼン

D. Sarasate

SENTO NEL CORE

わが胸を

A. Scarlatti

SE FLORINDO È FEDELE

もしフロリンドが誠実ならば

A. Scarlatti

SYMPHONY No.8-UNFINISHED (1st Movement)

F. Schubert

未 完 成

SYMPHONY No.8-UNFINISHED (2nd Movement)

F. Schubert

MOMENTS MUSICAUX Op.94 No.3

F. Schubert

楽興の時

202

MILITARY MARCH
軍隊行進曲

F. Schubert

IMPROMPTUS Op.142 No.3
即興曲

F. Schubert

IMPROMPTUS Op.90 No.3

F. Schubert

IMPROMPTUS Op.90 No.4

F. Schubert

WINTERREISE—GUTE NACHT

F. Schubert

おやすみ

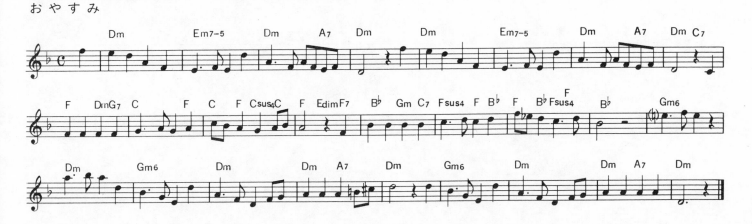

IMPROMPTUS Op.90 No.2

F. Schubert

IMPROMPTUS Op.90 No.1

F. Schubert

STRINGS QUARTET—DER TOD UND DAS MÄDCHEN (1st Movement)

F. Schubert

死とおとめ

STRINGS QUARTET—DER TOD UND DAS MÄDCHEN (2nd Movement)

F. Schubert

WINTERREISE—DER LINDENBAUM

F. Schubert

ぼ だ い 樹

WINTERREISE—WASSERFLUT

F. Schubert

あふれる涙

WINTERREISE—FRÜHLINGSTRAUM

F. Schubert

春 の 夢

WINTERREISE—DER WEGWEISER
F. Schubert

道しるべ

WINTERREISE—DER LEIERMANN
F. Schubert

つじ音楽師

ROSAMUNDE
F. Schubert

ロザムンデ

Andantino

208

DIE SCHÖNE MÜLLERIN—DAS WANDERN
さすらい

F. Schubert

DIE SCHÖNE MÜLLERIN—WOHIN
どこへ

F. Schubert

DIE SCHÖNE MÜLLERIN—TROCKNE BLUMEN
しぼんだ花

F. Schubert

209

SERENADE
セレナーデ

F. Schubert

AVE MARIA
アヴェ・マリア

F. Schubert

DIE FORELLE

ます

F. Schubert

AN DIE MUSIK

楽に寄す

F. Schubert

HEIDENRÖSLEIN

野 ばら

F. Schubert

WIEGENLIED

子守歌

F. Schubert

SYMPHONIE No.3 "RHEINISCHE" (1st Movement)

R. Schumann

ラ　イ　ン

PIANO CONCERTO (1st Movement)

R. Schumann

PIANO CONCERTO (2nd Movement)

R. Schumann

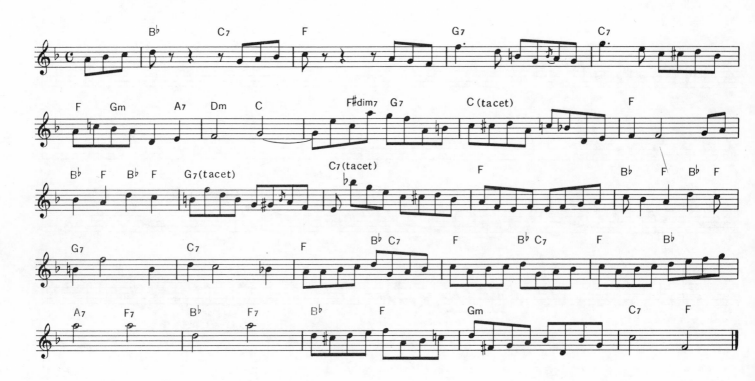

FRÖHLICHER LANDMANN

R. Schumann

楽しき農夫

CARNAVAL—PRÉAMBULE

R. Schumann

謝肉祭―前口上

CARNAVAL—RECONNAISSANCE

R. Schumann

感　謝

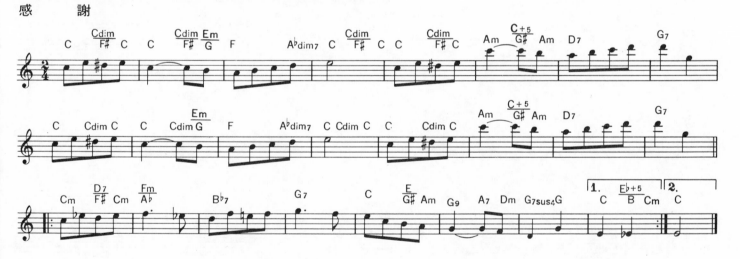

THEMA UND VARIATIONEN ÜBER DEN NAMEN ABEGG

R. Schumann

アベッグ変奏曲

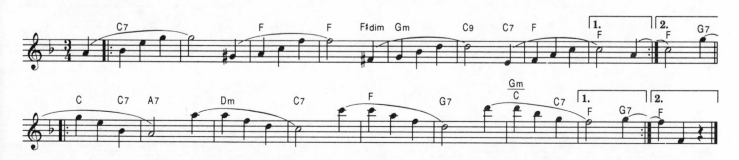

214

CARNAVAL—VALSE ALLEMANDE

R. Schumann

ドイツ風円舞曲

CARNAVAL—AVEU

R. Schumann

告　白

VON FREMDEN LÄNDERN UND MENSCHEN

R. Schumann

子どもの情景―知らない国々

TRÄUMEREI

R. Schumann

トロイメライ

AM KAMIN

R. Schumann

炉ばたで

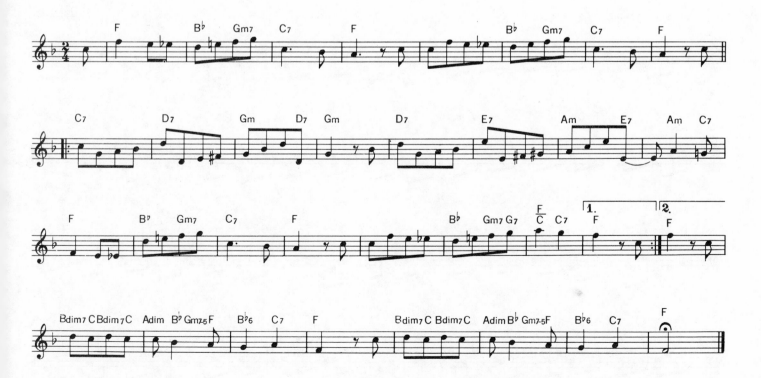

PAPILLONS
胡　蝶

R. Schumann

WIEGENLIED
子　守歌

R. Schumann

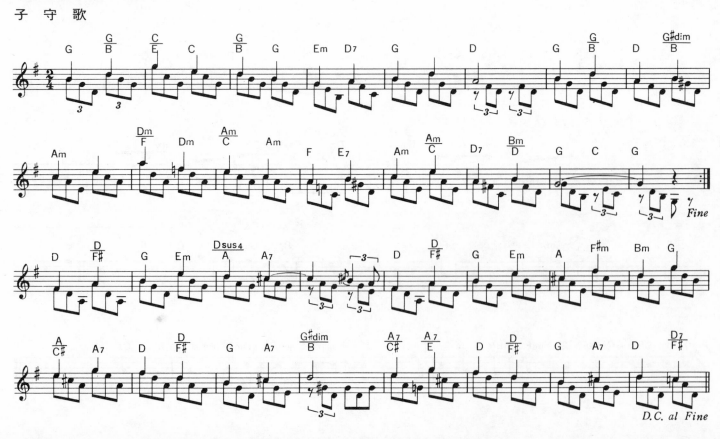

DIE BEIDEN GRENADIERE

F. Schubert

二人のてき弾兵

IM WUNDERSCHÖNEN MONAT MAI

F. Schubert

詩人の恋—美しき五月

WIDMUNG

ミルテの花―献呈

F. Schubert

DU RING AN MEINEM FINGER

女の愛と生涯―指輪

F. Schubert

DIE LORELEI

ローレライ

F. Silcher

MY COUNTRY No.2—MOLDAU

モルダウ

B. Smetana

POLKA

B. Smetana

SLOVAKIAN POLKA

スロバキアン・ダンス

B. Smetana

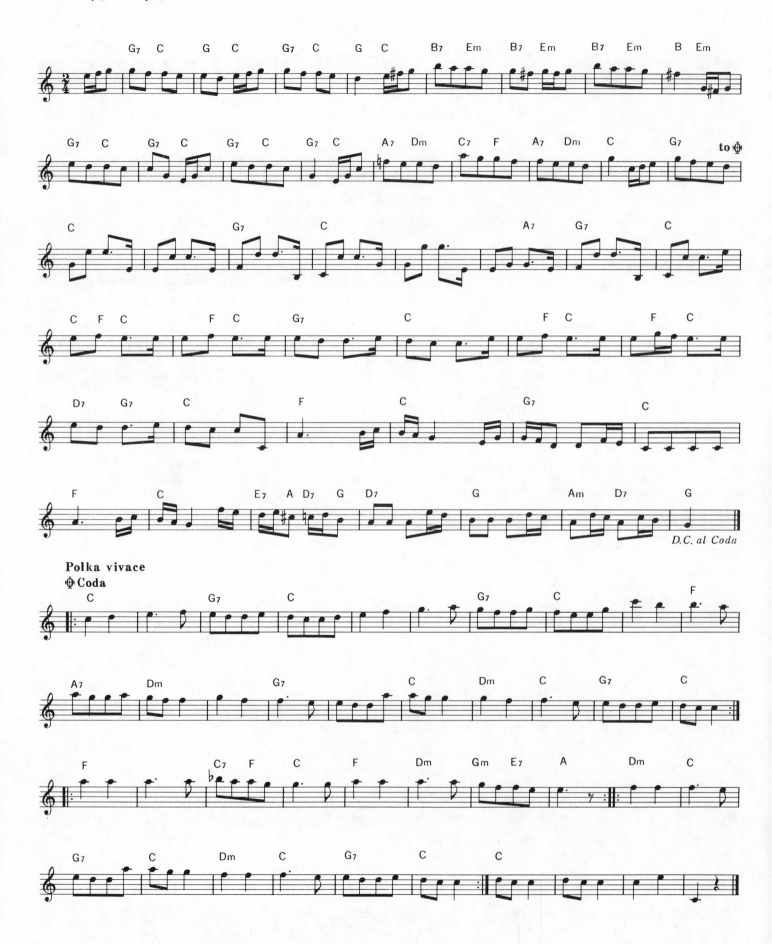

THE STARS AND STRIPES FOREVER

星条旗よ永遠なれ

J. P. Sousa

222

THE WASINGTON POST

ワシントン・ポスト

J. P. Sousa

THE THUNDERER

雷　神

J. P. Sousa

THE HIGH SCHOOL CADETS

J. P. Sousa

士官候補生

THE FAIREST OF THE FAIR

美中の美

J. P. Sousa

PIZZICATO POLKA
ピチカート・ポルカ

J. Strauss

WIENENER BLUT
ウィーンかたぎ

J. Strauss

KÜNSTLER-LEBEN
芸術家の生涯

J. Strauss

ROSEN AUS DEM SÜDEN

南国のばら

J. Strauss

FRÜHLINGSSTIMMEN

春 の 声

J. Strauss

ANNEN POLKA

アンネン・ポルカ

J. Strauss

KAISER WALZER

皇帝円舞曲

J. Strauss

MORNING PAPERS

朝 の 新 聞

J. Strauss

TRISCH-TRASCH POLKA

トリッチ・トラッチ・ポルカ

J. Strauss

AN DER SHÖNEN BLAUEN DONAU

美しく青きドナウ

J. Strauss

DIE FLEDERMAUS-OVERTURE

J. Strauss

こうもり―序曲

Tempo di Valse

GESCHICHTEN AUS DEN WIENERWARD

J. Strauss

ウィーンの森の物語

POET AND PEASANT

F. v. Suppe

詩人と農夫

LIGHT CAVALRY

F. v. Suppe

軽騎兵

RECUERDOS DE LA ALHAMBRA

アルハンブラの想い出

F. Tarrega

SYMPHONIE No.4 (1st Movement)

P. I. Tchaikovsky

SYMPHONIE No.4 (3rd Movement)

P. I. Tchaikovsky

SYMPHONY No.5 (1st Movement)

P. I. Tchaikovsky

SYMPHONY No.5 (2nd Movement)

P. I. Tchaikovsky

240

SYMPHONY No.5 (3rd Movement)

P. I. Tchaikovsky

SYMPHONY No.6-PATHÉTIQUE (1st Movement)

P. I. Tchaikovsky

悲　愴

SYMPHONY No.6-PATHÉTIQUE (2nd Movement)

P. I. Tchaikovsky

SWAN LAKE (SCENE I)

白鳥の湖―情景 I

P. I. Tchaikovsky

SWAN LAKE—DANCES DES CYGNES

P. I. Tchaikovsky

白鳥の踊り

SWAN LAKE—VALSE

P. I. Tchaikovsky

円 舞 曲

SWAN LAKE (SCENE II)

情 景 II

P. I. Tchaikovsky

SWAN LAKE—DANCE HONGROISE (CZARDAS)

チャルダッシュ

P. I. Tchaikovsky

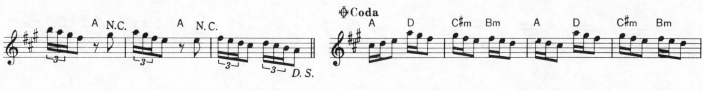

CASSE-NOISETTE—DANCE DE LA FÉE-DRAGÉE

P. I. Tchaikovsky

くるみ割り人形—こんぺい糖の踊り

CASSE-NOISETTE—OUVERTURE

P. I. Tchaikovsky

序　曲

CASSE-NOISETTE—VALSE DES FLEURS

P. I. Tchaikovsky

花のワルツ

CASSE-NOISETTE—DANCE RUSSE

P. I. Tchaikovsky

ロシアの踊り―トレパーク

CASSE-NOISETTE—DANCE DES MIRLITONS

P. I. Tchaikovsky

あし笛の踊り

CASSE-NOISETTE—MARCHE

P. I. Tchaikovsky

行 進 曲

CASSE-NOISETTE DANSE ARABE

P. I. Tchaikovsky

アラビアの踊り

Allegretto Comodo

CASSE-NOISETTE DANSE CHINOISE

P. I. Tchaikovsky

中国の踊り

Allegro Moderato

THE SLEEPING BEAUTY—WALTZ

眠りの森の美女　ワルツ

P. I. Tchaikovsky

ROMEO AND JULIET

ロミオとジュリエット

P. I. Tchaikovsky

OUVERTURE SOLENNELLE "1812"

1812年

P. I. Tchaikovsky

CAPRICE ITARIENNE

P. I. Tchaikovsky

イタリア奇想曲

VIOLIN CONCERTO (1st Movement)

P. I. Tchaikovsky

VIOLIN CONCERTO (2nd Movement)

P. I. Tchaikovsky

VIOLIN CONCERTO (3rd Movement)

P. I. Tchaikovsky

PIANO CONCERTO No.1 (1st Movement)

P. I. Tchaikovsky

PIANO CONCERTO No.1 (2nd Movement)

P. I. Tchaikovsky

Andante Semlios

PIANO TRIO IN A MINOR, Op.50
"TO THE MEMORY OF A GREAT ARTIST"

P. I. Tchaikovsky

偉大な芸術家の思い出に

SERENADE C Dur (1st Movement)

P. I. Tchaikovsky

弦楽セレナード

Andante non troppo

SERENADE C Dur (2nd Movement)

CHANT SANS PAROLES

無言歌

P. I. Tchaikovsky

TROIKA

トロイカ

P. I. Tchaikovsky

BARCAROLLE
舟　歌

P. I. Tchaikovsky

ANCIENNE CHANSON FRANÇAISE
フランスの古い歌

P. I. Tchaikovsky

MARCH SLAV
スラブ・マーチ

P. I. Tchaikovsky

STRING QUARTET—ANDANTE CANTABILE

P. I. Tchaikovsky

アンダンテ・カンタービレ

CHANSON TRISTE
悲しい歌

P. I. Tchaikovsky

PLEASANT DREAMS
すてきな夢

P. I. Tchaikovsky

MORNING PRAYER
朝の祈り

P. I. Tchaikovsky

258

ALTE KAMERADEN
旧　　友

K. Teike

MIGNON—GAVOTTE
ミニヨン—ガボット

A. Thomas

RAYMOND OVERTURE

レイモンド—序曲

A. Thomas

Moderato

SERENATA RIMPIANT
嘆きのセレナード

E. Toselli

IDEALE
理想の人

F. P. Tosti

SOGNO

夢

F. P. Tosti

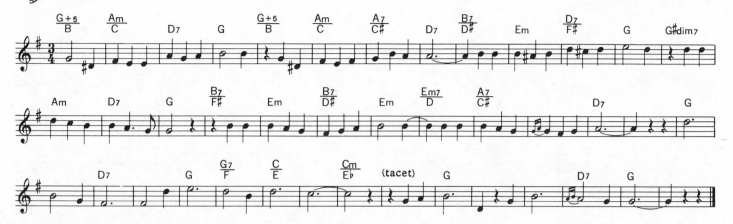

LA SERENATA

セレナータ

F. P. Tosti

MARECHIARE

マレキアーレ

F. P. Tosti

262

AIDA TRIUMPHAL MARCH

アイーダ―凱旋行進曲

G. Verdi

AIDA CELESTE AIDA

清きアイーダ

G. Verdi

AIDA GRAND MARCH

グランド・マーチ

G. Verdi

TROVATORE ANVIL CHORUS

トロヴァトーレ―アンヴィル・コーラス

G. Verdi

TROVATORE STRIDE-LA VAMPA!

G. Verdi

炎は燃えて

TROVATORE MISERERE

G. Verdi

ミゼレレ

RIGOLETTO—LA DONNA E MOBILE

G. Verdi

女心の唄

LA TRAVIATA—AH FORS'E LUI CHE L'ANIMA

G. Verdi

椿姫—ああ、そはかの人か

LA TRAVIATA—PARIGI, O CARA

G. Verdi

パリを離れて

266

LA TRAVIATA—DI PROVANZA IL MAR

G. Verdi

プロバンスの海に

LA TRAVIATA-BRINDISI

G. Verdi

乾杯の歌

LA TRAVIATA PRELUDO

G. Verdi

前 奏 曲

UNTER DEM DOPPELADLER

J. F. Wagner

双頭の鷲の旗の下に

LE QUATTRO STAGIONI—LA PRIMAVERA (1st Movement)

A. Vivaldi

四季から 春 第1楽章

LE QUATTRO STAGIONI—L'ESTATE (1st Movement)

A. Vivaldi

四季から 夏 第1楽章

LE QUATTRO STAGIONI—L'AUTUNNO (1st Movement)

A. Vivaldi

四季から 秋 第1楽章

LE QUATTRO STAGIONI—L'INVERNO (2nd Movement)

A. Vivaldi

四季から 冬 第2楽章

LOHENGRIN—BRIDAL MARCH

R. Wagner

結婚行進曲

WALKÜRENRITT

R. Wagner

ワルキューレの騎行

TANNHÄUSER MARCH

タンホイザー・マーチ

R. Wagner

TANNHÄUSER EVENING STAR

夕星の歌

R. Wagner

THE SKATERS WALTZES

スケーター・ワルツ

E. Waldteufel

ESTUDIANTINA

女学生

E. Waldteufel

ESPANA WALTZES

スペイン・ワルツ

E. Waldteufel

Andantino quasi Allegretto

BELLA BOCCA POLKA

ベェラ・ポッカ・ポルカ

E. Waldteufel

Allegretto

INVITATION TO THE DANCE (A)

C. M. v. Weber

舞踊への勧誘

INVITATION TO THE DANCE (B)

C. M. v. Weber

DER FREISCHÜTZ OVERTURE

C. M. v. Weber

魔弾の射手—序曲

DER FREISCHÜTZ JÄGERCHOR

C. M. v. Weber

狩人の合唱

AUF DEM WASSER

C. M. v. Weber

舟　　歌

HEIDENRÖSLEIN

H. Werner

野 ば ら

HER BRIGHT SMILE HAUNTS ME STILL

W. T. Wrighton

忘れ得ぬきみの微笑

SILVERY WAVES

A. Wyman

銀 の 波

Great Music at Your Fingertips